NICK DICK AND TH...

Drugs were get...
The Customs m...

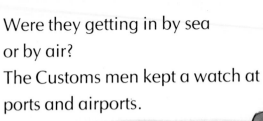

Were they getting in by sea
or by air?
The Customs men kept a watch at
ports and airports.

Nick Dick the detective was called in.
She had an idea the drugs were getting
in by sea.

So each day she went to a port.
She went and looked at the boats.

One day she saw a big Spanish fishing
boat out at sea.
It was fishing but it did not
come into port.

The next week the Spanish fishing boat
was there again.
Nick Dick watched it but it did not
come into port.

The next week it was there again.
Nick Dick had an idea, so she watched.

She watched the men putting the nets
into the sea.
By the beach a man was fishing in
a small boat.

The man in the small boat kept looking over the side.
Nick Dick watched the men pulling the nets into the big fishing boat.

Nick Dick went down to the beach.
She waited for the man in the
small boat to come in.

The small boat was full of drugs!
She arrested the man.

But how had the drugs got into
the small boat?
Nick Dick went out with the Customs
man to the Spanish fishing boat.

There were no drugs on the boat.
But there were some fish.

The fish were in a big tank.
They were dolphins!

The fishermen had trained the
dolphins.
They had trained them to swim with
the drugs.

The Customs men were very pleased.
Nick Dick had solved yet another
crime.